MARTIN POWELL
WRITER

FRED CARRILLO
PENCILER
INKER (p. 1-23, 81-92)

SERGIO CARIELLO (p. 55-65)
STEVE MITCHELL (p. 24-40)
RODNEY RAMOS (p. 41-54)
DAVE SIMONS (p. 66-80)
INKERS

BRAD K. JOYCE
LETTERER

ED LAZELLARI
MARIA PARWULSKI
GREG ROSEWALL
COLORISTS

LESLIE PETERSON
EDITORIAL ASSISTANT

LIA PELOSI
ASSISTANT EDITOR

DARRYL WINBURNE
CONSULTING EDITOR

H. MESNIK
R. WITTERSTAETTER
EDITORS

TOM DeFALCO
EDITOR IN-CHIEF

3

I'M...OUT OF A JOB, AND I *HOPED* THAT PERHAPS YOU MIGHT BE ABLE TO *HELP* ME...?

I'M AFRAID I DON'T KNOW OF ANYTHING. JOBS ARE *SCARCE*. NOW IF YOU'LL EXCUSE ME --

PLEASE, REVEREND... P-PLEASE...

...I-I THOUGHT THAT MAYBE *YOU* MIGHT HAVE SOMETHING FOR ME TO DO...? SOME PAINTING OR ROOFING, PERHAPS?

I'M *SORRY*, SON. THERE'S NOTHING FOR YOU HERE. PLEASE EXCUSE ME NOW, I'M EXTREMELY *BUSY* THIS MORNING.

GOD BLESS. YOU.

TH-THANK YOU, SIR.

HENRY...WHO WAS THAT *DREADFUL* CREATURE?

ONLY A TRAMP. WHERE'D YOU GO SO EARLY THIS MORNING?

I WAS VISITING MRS. DOBBING; THE POOR DEAR'S STILL NOT FEELING WELL. DID YOU FINISH YOUR *SERMON*?

NO. NOT YET.

I WAS... *INTERRUPTED*.

FIRST CHURCH OF RAYMOND, SUNDAY MORNING SERVICE.

"...HE SAID 'WHAT YOU DO TO YOUR NEIGH--BOR...DO AS YOU WOULD UN--TO ME...'"

"...HE SAID WE SHOULD TREAT STRANGERS KIND-LY..."

"...FOR HE SAID THAT THE STRAN--GER IS HE."

AHHHHH...MEN

MY DEAR FRIENDS IN CHRIST, I BELIEVE OUR SISTER RACHEL'S BEAUTIFUL HYMN IS AN APPROPRIATE AND HOLY PREFACE TO THIS MORNING'S SERMON...

...THAT OF *FOLLOWING CHRIST*, HIS SACRIFICE AND EXAMPLE, IN OUR DAILY LIVES!

6

...LONG BEFORE I CAME IN HERE...!

THERE...THERE'S NO NEED TO BE AFRAID OF ME. I'M *NOT DRUNK* OR CRAZY, AND I'M PERFECTLY *HARMLESS.*

I'M HERE ONLY TO...TO TELL YOU SOMETHING.

THAT'S ALL.

≥KOFF≥
≥KOFF≥

UGHH

YOU'RE VERY ILL--! YOU SHOULD BE IN A *HOSPITAL!*

NO...

NO.

IT'S...MUCH *TOO LATE* FOR THAT.

I...I'M *DYING.*

I *KNOW* THAT I AM. AND...I WANT THE *SATISFACTION* OF HAVING MY SAY IN A PLACE LIKE *THIS...*

...AND BEFORE THIS SORT OF *CROWD.*

7

I... I'M *NOT* AN ORDINARY TRAMP...

DO YOU?

...ALTHOUGH I DON'T KNOW OF ANY TEACHINGS OF JESUS THAT MAKES ONE KIND OF TRAMP LESS WORTH SAVING THAN ANOTHER.

I *LOST* MY JOB TEN MONTHS AGO.

I'M A PRINTER BY TRADE, AND I DON'T BLAME THE NEWSPAPERS FOR CONVERTING TO THE NEW *LINOTYPE MACHINES*-- THEY REALLY ARE WONDERFUL INVENTIONS...

...BUT WHAT CAN A MAN DO WHEN HE KNOWS *ONLY* ONE SKILL?

I'VE WANDERED FOR *NEARLY A YEAR*, LOOKING FOR SOME- THING--*ANYTHING*... AND IN ALL THAT TIME I HAVEN'T HEARD A *SINGLE WORD* OF SYMPATHY OR COMFORT!

AND THERE ARE MANY, *MANY MORE* JUST LIKE *ME!*

I DON'T *BLAME* ANYBODY, BUT I'M *PUZZLED* BY HOW YOU CAN *SING* AND *PRAY* THE WAY YOU DO...?

WHAT DO YOU *MEAN* BY IT--?

HAVE ANY OF YOU EVER *TRULY* SACRIFICED AND DENIED YOUR- SELVES TO SAVE EVEN ONE LOST AND *SUFFERING* CREATURE--?!

IT'S *TOO LATE* FOR ME...BUT THERE MUST BE OVER A *HUNDRED* MEN LIKE ME IN YOUR TOWN--AND MOST OF THEM HAVE *FAMILIES!*

MY...MY OWN WIFE *DIED*...FOUR MONTHS AGO.

I'M GLAD HER *SUFFERING* IS OVER.

OUR LITTLE GIRL WAS TAKEN FROM US....⸘KOFF⸘...AWAY TO AN *ORPHAN ASYLUM*... BUT NOT BEFORE SHE HEARD HER MOTHER GASP FOR BREATH, STARVING AND FREEZING IN OUR NEW YORK CITY TENEMENT.

THEN...WHEN OUR SAVINGS RAN OUT, WE WERE *EVICTED*... ALTHOUGH THE LANDLORD *KNEW* THAT MY WIFE WAS ILL. AND HE WAS-- JUST LIKE ALL OF YOU-- A *CHURCHGOER*...!

⸘KOFF⸘ ⸘KOFF⸘

I ASK YOU... *ALL OF YOU* ...⸘KOFF-.-K-KOFF⸘... IS *THAT* WHAT IT MEANS... ...⸘KOFF⸘...

...TO...

...FOLLOW...

...JES--US...

...⸘...

...UHHHHH...

AH, GOOD EVENING, RACHEL. I'M HAPPY YOU'VE BROUGHT MORE SOUP. OUR FRIEND IS *PERILOUSLY MALNOURISHED.*

WILL HE MAKE IT, DR. WEST?

THE FEVER HAS PASSED, BUT HIS *HEART* IS VERY WEAK. HE KNOWS HE HASN'T MUCH TIME LEFT, AND SOMEHOW HAS FOUND *PEACE* WITH THAT.

HOW...HOW *TERRIBLE.* GOD HELP HIM.

"I HOPE SO, BUT I'M AFRAID THERE'S NOTHING MORE *WE* CAN DO."

¤Z!?¿

11

I'M SORRY, REVEREND. I DIDN'T MEAN TO STARTLE YOU.

WHY DON'T YOU GO LIE DOWN? I'LL SIT WITH OUR FRIEND FOR A WHILE. YOU'VE DONE *MORE* THAN ENOUGH TONIGHT.

"YOU...YOU'VE BEEN *GOOD* TO ME, REVEREND. SOMEHOW...I FEEL THIS IS JUST WHAT *JESUS* WOULD'VE DONE."

LORD FORGIVE ME...

...IF ONLY THAT WERE *TRUE.*

12

THE NEXT MORNING...

HE IS GONE.

SINCE OUR BROTHER PASSED AWAY, I'VE LEARNED A BIT MORE OF HIS HISTORY. HE HAS A SISTER LIVING IN CHICAGO, AND I'VE WRITTEN TO HER, BUT I'VE YET TO RECEIVE A REPLY.

HIS LITTLE GIRL IS WITH MY WIFE AND I, AND WILL REMAIN FOR THE TIME.

SINCE LAST SUNDAY, THE SIMPLE WORDS OF THIS STRANGER HAVE MADE A VERY *POWERFUL* IMPRESSION ON ME. NEVER BEFORE, IN MY LIFE AS A MINISTER, HAVE I BEEN SO *COMPELLED* BY HIS INNOCENT QUESTION...

..."WHAT DOES FOLLOWING JESUS *MEAN?*"

13

BEFORE WE CAN TRULY CALL OURSELVES *CHRISTIANS*, IT IS ABSOLUTELY NECESSARY TO *ANSWER* THAT MOST IMPORTANT QUESTION.

AND THERE HAS NEVER BEEN A TIME MORE APPROPRIATE THAN THE *PRESENT*.

TO SPEAK BLUNTLY, I WANT *VOLUNTEERS* FROM THIS CHURCH TO PLEDGE THEMSELVES, EARNESTLY AND HONESTLY, FOR AN *ENTIRE YEAR*, NOT TO DO ANYTHING WITHOUT FIRST ASKING THE QUESTION...

"...WHAT WOULD JESUS DO?"

EACH VOLUNTEER WILL THEN FOLLOW THE EXAMPLE OF JESUS AS *EXACTLY* AS HE, OR SHE, KNOWS HOW--NO MATTER WHAT THE PERSONAL RESULTS OR THE CONSEQUENCES OF THEIR ACTIONS.

I WILL, OF COURSE, INCLUDE *MYSELF* IN THIS COMPANY.

ALL THOSE WISHING TO VOLUNTEER PLEASE REMAIN, AND WE'LL DISCUSS THE DETAILS OF OUR PLAN.

OUR SERVICE IS NOW CLOSED.

I *TRIED*, MY POOR FRIEND. I TRIED TO GIVE SOME *MEANING* TO YOUR SAD PASSING. NOW MY SERMON IS OVER ...

...AND *NO ONE* HAS REMAINED TO JOIN ME.

NO DOUBT MANY OF THEM THINK SUCH A PROPOSAL IS *IMPOSSIBLE*.

BUT I *DON'T* BELIEVE THAT.

NOR DO *WE*, REVEREND.

--?!

YOU...YOU CAME...!

WE NEEDED TIME TO THINK. BY THE TIME WE MADE UP OUR MINDS, YOU'D LEFT THE CHURCH, BUT WE KNEW YOU'D BE HERE.

SPEAKING FOR THE GROUP OF US, REVEREND MAXWELL ...

...WE WANT TO *VOLUNTEER*.

15

LATER THAT WEEK...

"MR. NORMAN--THAT'S **OUTRAGEOUS!** IT'S TOTALLY **UNHEARD OF!** YOU **CAN'T MEAN IT!!**"

DAILY NEWS

EDWARD NORMAN
PUBLISHER.

I'LL SAY IT AGAIN, CLARK, WE WON'T BE PRINTING THIS STORY. LEAVE IT **OUT.**

GO TO PRESS WITHOUT A WORD ON LAST NIGHT'S **PRIZE FIGHT--?!** ALL THE OTHER PAPERS WILL RUN THE STORY! WHAT WILL OUR **SUBSCRIBERS** SAY?

CLARK, IF **CHRIST** WAS THE **PUBLISHER** OF THIS PAPER, DO YOU HONESTLY THINK HE'D PRINT THREE COLUMNS GLORIFYING SUCH **CORRUPTION AND VIOLENCE?**

HUH--?!

I UNDERSTAND ONE OF THOSE FIGHTERS WAS NEARLY **BEATEN TO DEATH--**WHILE THE CROWD **CHEERED!**

I'VE TAKEN A **VOW** NOT TO DO ANYTHING FOR A **WHOLE YEAR** THAT I HONESTLY BELIEVE JESUS WOULDN'T DO.

YOU...YOU **CAN'T** BE SERIOUS!

IT ISN'T FEASIBLE TO RUN A PAPER LIKE THIS! IT'LL **RUIN** OUR BUSINESS!

NEVERTHELESS, THE REPORT WILL NOT GO IN.

NOW GET ME THE ADDRESSES OF OUR **TOBACCO AND ALCOHOL** ADVERTISERS.

I WANT TO SEND SOME **TELEGRAMS.**

17

WELL, MR. NORMAN--? SURELY YOU AREN'T *SURPRISED*?

IN LESS THAN TEN HOURS WE'VE LOST THE ACCOUNTS OF OVER *TWO DOZEN* MAJOR ADVERTISERS, AND MANY OF THEM ARE EVEN CANCELLING THEIR SUBSCRIPTIONS! WHAT'RE YOU TRYING TO PROVE?

CLARK, DO YOU THINK *JESUS* WOULD ADVOCATE THE USE OF WHISKEY AND CIGARS?

WELL... NO, I DON'T SUPPOSE HE WOULD.

BUT, IF WE CONTINUE IN THIS FASHION, THE DAILY NEWS WILL GO *BANKRUPT* IN THIRTY DAYS!

I *DISAGREE* WITH YOU, CLARK. AND I'LL CONTINUE IN THIS MANNER WITH THE BELIEF THAT WE'LL NOT ONLY SUCCEED, BUT THAT WE'LL PROSPER *GREATER* THAN WE EVER HAVE BEFORE.

BE PATIENT. YOU'RE A GOOD NEWS EDITOR, AND I HOPE YOU'LL STAY WITH ME.

WE'LL TALK ABOUT THIS AGAIN TOMORROW.

18

HELLO, GEORGE! WHAT'S THE MATTER HERE?

MR. NORMAN, SIR--!

THE BOYS AND ME, WELL, WE CAN'T SELL ANY OF OUR PAPERS TONIGHT!

ALL OUR CUSTOMERS WANTED NEWS ON THE PRIZE FIGHT, SO THEY WENT TO THE OTHER NEWSSTANDS!

REALLY, MR. NORMAN, SIR--IT AIN'T OUR FAULT! THE FIGHT JUST AIN'T IN OUR PAPERS!

DON'T WORRY, GEORGE.

HERE YOU ARE...

...I'LL BUY ALL YOUR PAPERS TONIGHT.

AND IF YOU EVER HAVE SIMILAR COMPLAINTS FROM YOUR REGULAR CUSTOMERS, I'LL BUY THOSE UNSOLD COPIES, TOO. IS THAT FAIR?

JEEPERS--! I--I MEAN SURE, MR. NORMAN! THAT'S SWELL!

THERE YOU ARE, EDWARD! I WAS GETTING WORRIED. WHAT KEPT YOU?

I STOPPED TO BUY SOME NEWSPAPERS.

19

THESE LETTERS AND TELEGRAMS HAVE BEEN ARRIVING ALL DAY. IS SOMETHING *WRONG*, EDWARD?

JUST A LITTLE EXPERIMENT WITH MY NEWSPAPER, ANNA, MY DEAR.

THAT'S ALL.

WELL, I COULD TELL MOST OF THEM WERE *COMPLAINTS*, THREATENING TO CANCEL THEIR PAPERS, AND--

AHH~!

EDWARD--? EDWARD, WHAT IS IT? ARE...ARE YOU *CRYING*...?

IT...IT'S NOTHING, ANNA. PLEASE, MY DEAR, DON'T TROUBLE YOURSELF.

BUT--BUT THAT *LETTER*--

MERELY A NOTE FROM AN OLD FRIEND...

...TELLING ME HE IS RATHER *PLEASED* WITH THE WORK I'VE DONE!

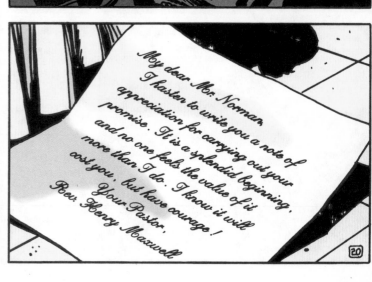

My dear Mr. Norman,
I hasten to write you a note of appreciation for carrying out your promise. It is a splendid beginning, and no one feels the value of it more than I do. I know it will cost you, but have courage!
Your Pastor,
Rev. Henry Maxwell

20

NEXT SUNDAY...

THE *SPIRIT* TRULY MOVED THAT SERMON, REVEREND! NOT NEAR ENOUGH IS SPOKEN OUT AGAINST THE *HYPOCRISY* OF THE CHURCH-GOING COMMUNITY!

IN FACT, I THINK I'LL WRITE AN *EDITORIAL* IN THE MORNING EDITION UPON THAT VERY SUBJECT!

DELIGHTED TO HEAR IT, MR. NORMAN. SUCH AN ARTICLE IN THE DAILY NEWS WOULD CERTAINLY BE WELCOME, ALONG WITH THE OTHER *REMARKABLE* CHANGES YOU'VE CREATED SINCE OUR *PLEDGE*!

HOW HAS YOUR *DIS-CONTINUANCE* OF THE SUNDAY PAPER AFFECTED YOU FINANCIALLY, EDWARD?

IT'S A BIT EARLY TO SAY, ALEX. SUBSCRIPTIONS AND ADVERTISEMENTS HAVE FALLEN OFF, BUT I ANTICIPATED THAT.

DO YOU REGRET THIS LATEST ACTION?

NOT AT ALL. I AM PERFECTLY SATISFIED THAT JESUS WOULD *NEVER* ISSUE A SUNDAY NEWSPAPER.

I CONFESS, HOWEVER, THAT TRYING TO RUN THE DAILY NEWS THE WAY I BELIEVE OUR LORD WOULD DO SO IS NOT AN *EASY* TASK TO ACCOMPLISH!

I'M HAVING THE SAME *TROUBLE.*

OUR PLEDGE IS ESPECIALLY CONFUSING TO ME BECAUSE OF MY *MONEY.* CHRIST NEVER OWNED ANY PROPERTY, AND THERE IS NOTHING IN HIS EXAMPLE TO GUIDE ME. I MEAN, WHAT WOULD HE DO WITH A *MILLION DOLLARS?*

YOU'RE NOT ALONE, GINNY.

WE'VE *ALL* VOWED THAT THE SAVIOR'S ACTIONS SHOULD INFLUENCE THE ENTIRE COURSE OF OUR LIVES, IN EVERY WAY, INCLUDING THE USE OF WHATEVER PERSONAL GIFTS WE EACH POSSESS.

IN TIME I BELIEVE WE ALL WILL *UNDERSTAND.*

LATER THAT WEEK...

"PLEASE, DON'T BE UNCOMFORTABLE, REVEREND MAXWELL..."

L&R RAILRO

...I ASKED YOU HERE SIMPLY TO *TALK* TO MY MEN, NOT TO PREACH.

I REALLY FEEL THAT, GIVEN THE OPPORTUNITY, YOU COULD BE A GREAT COMFORT TO THEM.

BUT THESE MEN ARE *LABORERS,* MR. POWERS--ENTIRELY REMOVED FROM *CHURCH INFLUENCE!* WHAT COULD I POSSIBLY HAVE TO SAY TO THEM--?!

L&R RAILROAD

ALEXANDER POWERS SUPERINTENDENT

FOLLOW ME UPSTAIRS, REVEREND, AND I'LL SHOW YOU WHAT I'M TRYING TO DO.

SINCE MAKING OUR *PLEDGE* A WEEK AGO, I'VE HAD A GOOD MANY THINGS TO THINK ABOUT...

...AND AMONG THOSE THINGS IS *THIS* !

I ASKED THE COMPANY FOR USE OF THIS SPARE ROOM, THEN SUPPLIED THE FURNITURE AND COFFEE MYSELF.

THESE MEN WORK *HARD*, REVEREND, FOR LITTLE REWARD BEYOND THEIR WEEKLY PAY-CHECKS. I WANTED TO PROVIDE A CLEAN, WARM PLACE FOR THEM TO REST DURING THEIR LUNCH-BREAK.

I THINK THIS IS WHAT *JESUS* WOULD DO, ADDING A LITTLE MORE PHYSICAL AND SPIRITUAL COMFORT TO THEIR LIVES.

OF COURSE, I AGREE WITH YOU, AND I'LL SPEAK TO YOUR MEN IF IT WILL HELP THEM.

BUT I'LL NEED SOME TIME TO PREPARE. WHEN IS THEIR LUNCH BREAK?

AT *NOON*, REVEREND, AS USUAL.

IN FACT...

...I THINK I HEAR THEM COMING...

...NOW!

FELLOWS, I'VE ASKED MY GOOD FRIEND, REVEREND MAXWELL, TO COME HERE ONCE A WEEK AND LEAD YOU IN THE PRIVILEGE OF A FIFTEEN MINUTE CHAT OF ANY SUBJECT ON YOUR MINDS.

I'M SURE THESE TALKS WILL BE A REAL HELP IN YOUR LIVES, AND I HOPE TO SEE ALL OF YOU HERE AGAIN NEXT WEEK.

MR. POWERS--! PLEASE! ONE MOMENT...!

PLEASE...DON'T LEAVE. I DON'T KNOW WHAT TO SAY TO THEM! WHAT SHOULD I DO?!

I'M NOT SURE, REVEREND. WHAT WOULD JESUS DO...?

AHH... GOOD AFTERNOON, GENTLEMEN.

AHH...

...GENTLEMEN, I--I'M AFRAID...

...THAT YOUR BOSS, AHH, MR. POWERS, HAS LEFT ME AT A DISADVANTAGE.

24

YOU MEAN YOUR *SINGING OFFER?*

YES. I'M...NOT GOING TO ACCEPT IT.

BUT *WHY,* RACHEL--? THIS HAS ALWAYS BEEN YOUR *DEAREST DREAM!*

I KNOW...BUT--I JUST DON'T FEEL THAT SINGING WITH A NEW YORK OPERA COMPANY IS WHAT *CHRIST* WOULD DO.

DO YOU THINK I'M *WRONG?*

I BELIEVE REVEREND MAXWELL WAS WISE WHEN HE SAID WE MUST THINK AND ACT FOR *OURSELVES* IN THIS PLEDGE.

AT LEAST YOU'VE *DECIDED,* DEAR. I'M HAVING A *MUCH HARDER* TIME WITH MY OWN SET OF TROUBLES.

ARE YOU REALLY, GINNY?

OH YES. REALLY.

I KNOW THAT EVERYONE IN RAYMOND *ENVIES* ME. I CAN TRAVEL ABROAD, ANYWHERE I PLEASE, OR I CAN STAY HOME IN THIS MAGNIFICENT HOUSE.

I CAN INSTANTLY GRATIFY ANY WANT OR DESIRE, AND YET...

...SOMETIMES I FEEL LIKE THE MOST WICKED, SELFISH, AND *USELESS* CREATURE IN THE WORLD.

SINCE THE APPEARANCE OF THAT POOR, POOR MAN IN OUR CHURCH, I'VE NOT BEEN ABLE TO LOOK OUT OF THIS WINDOW WITHOUT A FEELING OF *HORROR...*

...AT WHAT I'VE *BECOME.*

27

THE NEXT MORNING...

GOOD MORNING, MISS VIRGINIA. MADAM AND YOUR BROTHER ARE AWAITING YOU AND YOUR GUEST IN THE EAST-WING DINING ROOM.

THANK YOU, KAREN.

SORRY, RACHEL. I REALLY THOUGHT ROLLIN WOULD BE AT HIS CLUB.

IT'S OKAY, GINNY. WHATEVER CAN'T BE CURED MUST BE ENDURED.

SO. THE TWO OF YOU DECIDED NOT TO SLEEP YOUR LIVES AWAY AFTERALL.

I APOLOGIZE, GRANDMOTHER.

RACHEL AND I WERE UP TALKING RATHER LATE LAST NIGHT.

I THOUGHT AS MUCH.

WONDERFUL TO SEE YOU AGAIN, RACHEL!

THANK YOU, ROLLIN. THAT'S VERY NICE.

HERE! LET ME GET YOUR CHAIR!

I'M AFRAID MY GRANDSON ISN'T ONE TO HIDE HIS ENTHUSIASM, RACHEL. HE IS LIKE HIS FATHER IN THAT WAY. REST HIS SOUL.

BUT REGARDING YOUR RECENT GOOD NEWS I FEEL HIS FASCINATION IS QUITE UNDERSTANDABLE.

WHEN WILL YOU BE LEAVING TO SIMS IN NEW YORK?

I...

...I'VE DECIDED TO DECLINE THE OFFER, MADAM PAGE.

PERFORMING ON THE STAGE ISN'T THE BEST THING FOR ME.

28

WHAT--?! YOU CAN'T BE *SERIOUS*!

YOU WERE *BORN* TO PERFORM! NO ONE IN RAYMOND HAS A *VOICE* LIKE YOURS!

ROLLIN, PLEASE...

MY DEAR, ROLLIN MAY BE RATHER *SPONTANEOUS*, BUT HE'D NEVER PAY AN *INSINCERE* COMPLIMENT, AND I, FOR ONCE, *AGREE* WITH HIM.

NOW THEN, WHAT IS THIS *NONSENSE* ABOUT REJECTING THE PROPOSAL? WHAT EXACTLY ARE YOUR *REASONS*?

IT--IT'S *NOT* NONSENSE, MADAME PAGE.

AND I HAVE NO OTHER REASON...

...EXCEPT A *CONVICTION* THAT *JESUS CHRIST* WOULD DO THE SAME THING.

HOW *ABSURD*!!

I DECLARE, CHILD! I NEVER KNEW YOU WERE SO *EMPTY-HEADED*!!

GRANDMOTHER, PLEASE DON'T--

RACHEL--?!

GET OUT OF MY WAY!

LET ME *ALONE*!!

29

RACHEL! PLEASE--!

LET GO OF ME!

I'M *SORRY* ABOUT *GRANDMOTHER.* SHE *ALWAYS* BELIEVES SHE'S RIGHT--AND *NEVER* THINKS OF ANYONE BUT *HERSELF!*

OH YES, EXCEPT FOR YOUR *SISTER,* I'D SAY THAT'S A *FAMILY TRAIT,* WOULDN'T *YOU,* ROLLIN?

RACHEL...I'VE *LOVED* YOU SINCE WE WERE *CHILDREN*--YOU *MUST'VE* KNOWN HOW I'VE FELT ALL THESE YEARS! NOW I...I *NEED* TO KNOW...

...DO YOU *EVER* THINK OF ME...?

YES. BUT ONLY TO WISH THAT YOU'D *LEAVE* ME ALONE!

31

YOU USED TO LOVE ME, RACHEL--I *KNOW* YOU DID!

DID I? PERHAPS YOU'RE RIGHT...BUT WE'RE *OLDER* NOW.

WHY ARE YOU TREATING ME LIKE THIS & WHAT IS *WRONG* WITH ME--?!

YOU HAVE *NO PURPOSE* IN LIFE, ROLLIN!

WHAT HAVE YOU DONE TO MAKE THE WORLD *BETTER*? ALL YOU CARE ABOUT IS TRAVELING AND LUXURY!

I COULD *NEVER* LOVE YOU!

NOT LIKE THIS!!

I... I'M NO WORSE THAN OTHER MEN...AND NOT SO BAD AS *MANY*.

STILL... I'M *GLAD* TO FINALLY KNOW YOUR REASONS.

32

I CAN CHANGE, RACHEL. I CAN CHANGE.

I HAD NO RIGHT TO SPEAK TO ROLLIN LIKE THAT, NO RIGHT TO JUDGE HIM. AFTER ALL, WHAT PURPOSE IN LIFE HAVE I HAD?

EXPENSIVE BOARDING SCHOOLS, MUSIC LESSONS IN EUROPE, AND NOW THE PROMISE OF A LUCRATIVE SINGING CAREER...

...IS THIS WHAT JESUS WOULD DO...?

...YES, I SEE. WELL, THANK YOU, MADAM PAGE. I APPRECIATE YOUR LETTING ME KNOW.

DON'T WORRY, I WILL. GOOD-BYE.

WELL, WELL, THERE YOU ARE, YOUNG LADY...

YOU HAVE A GREAT DEAL OF EXPLAINING TO DO!

33

"MY GOODNESS! IT NEVER SEEMS TO STOP *RAINING* THESE DAYS!"

REVEREND & MRS. HENRY MAXWELL

MAY I HELP YOU, AUNT MARY?

HEAVENS, NO, MY DEAR. I'LL TEND TO THESE.

PERHAPS YOU'D BEST PRACTICE AT THE PIANO, CHILD. RACHEL WINSLOW WILL BE HERE TOMORROW TO BEGIN YOUR *LESSONS*!

REALLY, UNCLE HENRY? OH, THANK YOU SO MUCH!

THAT'S JUST WHAT I *WANTED*!

I'LL BE GOOD ENOUGH TO PLAY IN CHURCH SOON!

JUST WAIT AND SEE!

YOU'RE VERY *GOOD* TO HER, HENRY.

NO BETTER THAN HER POOR FATHER WOULD'VE BEEN...*IF* HE'D BEEN ABLE TO DO SO.

IT'S ALEXANDER POWERS, MARY!

THAT NICE MR. POWERS OF THE RAILROAD?

THE SAME. AND HIS TROUBLE IS THE RESULT OF *OUR PLEDGE!*

I HAVE TO GO!

Daily News
L&R RAILROAD SUPERINTENDENT RESIGNS.

BACK AT THE WINSLOW'S...

THIS IS ABSURD!

WHAT AM I GOING TO DO WITH YOU, RACHEL--?!

YOU'RE A *FANATIC!!*

LOOK AT THESE!

THEY'RE LETTERS OF *CONGRATULATIONS* FOR YOUR *NEW CAREER!* THERE'S ONE FROM *EVERYBODY* IN THE FAMILY-- EVEN YOUR AUNT IRENE IN ENGLAND!

I-- I'M SORRY, MAMA.

OH RACHEL...MY *BABY*...I'M SO SORRY. I JUST CAN'T STAND THE THOUGHT OF YOU IN THAT *TERRIBLE PLACE!*

I'VE GOT TO, MAMA. IT'S TIME FOR ME TO FINALLY *RISK* SOMETHING OF MY-SELF-- FOR *STRANGERS.*

I TRULY BELIEVE I'M DOING THE *RIGHT* THING...

"...MAYBE FOR THE *FIRST TIME* IN MY LIFE."

I KNOW THIS'LL BE *DIFFICULT*, ALEX. WHAT WILL YOU DO?

L & R RAILROAD

ALEXANDER POWERS SUPERINTENDENT

YOU MEAN ANOTHER JOB? I HAVE NO PLANS YET.

AND YOU'RE *CERTAIN* THE RAILROAD IS INVOLVED IN *ILLEGAL* ACTIONS?

ILLEGAL *AND* UNETHICAL. I'D SURELY HAVE TO BE FIRED AFTER EXPOSING THE PLOT. I *QUIT* TO SAVE THEM THE TROUBLE.

I THINK JESUS WOULD DO THE SAME THING, DON'T YOU, REVEREND?

YES, I BELIEVE HE WOULD.

I'VE ALREADY ASKED, AND I DON'T THINK THE COMPANY WILL OBJECT TO YOUR WEEKLY TALKS WITH THE MEN.

I HOPE YOU'LL CONTINUE THEM.

YES, ALEX. OF COURSE, I WILL.

GOOD. I REALLY THINK IT MAKES A DIFFERENCE.

I... I'D BETTER BE GOING. SEE YOU THIS SUNDAY.

GOOD-BYE, ALEX.

GOD BLESS YOU.

L & R RAILROAD

38

40

EXCUSE ME, PLEASE. COULD YOU HELP US? MY FRIEND AND I ARE LOOKING FOR THE *WHITE CROSS STATION* HERE ON SAINT GEORGE STREET.

COULD SOMEONE DIRECT US THERE?

A GENTLEMAN WAS SUPPOSED TO MEET US--A *DOCTOR.* HAVE ANY OF YOU *SEEN* HIM?

DOCTOR--?

D'YA...D'YA SAY *DOCTOR...*?

YES! *DOCTOR WEST*--A TALL, MUSTACHED GENTLE-MAN! DID YOU *SEE* HIM?

S-SEE HIM 'BOUT *TWICE A WEEK...* AT THE *MISSION.* BEEN TRYIN' TA HELP ME WITH MY, UHH, MY HEADACHES.

NICE MAN...OLD FRIEND OF THE FAMILY...

...THAT IS...WH--WHEN I *HAD A FAMILY...*

OH DEAR GOD.

LOREEN--?

IS...IS THAT YOU--?!

HUhh...? WHO...?

V-VIRGINIA...?

WHITE CROSS STATION
CHRISTIAN MISSION
WELCOME EVERY ONE

WELCOME, SISTER! *GOD* HAS LED YOU HERE!

COME IN AND STAY WITH US!

LOREEN--*PLEASE!* DON'T BE AFRAID. WE ONLY WANT TO *HELP* YOU!

UHHhh--?

N-NO... ...*NO!!*

DON'T *LOOK* AT ME--! D-DON'T TOUCH ME!

THE POOR SOUL! SHE'S *FAINTED!*

DR. WEST IS PROBABLY STILL WITH THE LITTLE ZIMMERMAN BABY!

I'LL RUN AND FETCH THE NURSE!

WE'RE SORRY TO *DISRUPT* YOUR SERVICE, MA'AM. I AM VIRGINIA PAGE, AND THIS IS MY FRIEND, RACHEL WINSLOW.

WHY, YES, OF COURSE! DOCTOR WEST SAID YOU DEARS WOULD BE COMING TO HELP!

I'M MRS. GREY. MY HUSBAND AND I ARE VERY *GRATEFUL* THAT YOU'RE HERE!

WE *KNOW* THIS GIRL, MRS. GREY. HOW CAN WE FIND OUT WHERE SHE LIVES?

I DARE SAY THE POOR CHILD *HASN'T* A HOME, MY DEAR. SHE'S BEEN LIVING IN DOORWAYS THE PAST SEVERAL MONTHS, TOO *PROUD* TO ACCEPT CHARITY.

THEN...WHAT WILL BECOME OF HER? ISN'T THERE A DECENT BOARDING HOUSE WHERE SHE CAN STAY?

THAT ISN'T NECESSARY, RACHEL. WE *CAN'T* LEAVE LOREEN LIKE THIS.

I'M TAKING HER HOME...WITH *ME.*

LATER

YOU'RE *WHAT~?!*

44

I WON'T SPEND ANOTHER HOUR BENEATH THIS ROOF!

IF YOU FAVOR THAT DRUNKEN HARLOT OVER YOUR OWN GRANDMOTHER--

--SO BE IT!!

GOOD RIDDANCE, IF YOU ASK ME. SHE'S BEEN FREELOADING HERE LONG ENOUGH.

ROLLIN--!

YOU DON'T BLAME ME, DO YOU? AM I WRONG?

NO, SIS. I DON'T BELIEVE YOU ARE.

YOU KNOW, I DIDN'T UNDERSTAND THIS PLEDGE OF YOURS BEFORE, BUT NOW I'M STARTING TO SEE THINGS DIFFERENTLY.

"FOR YEARS I'VE SELFISHLY ENJOYED EVERY LUXURY IMAGINABLE... FORGETFUL OF THE TERRIBLE POVERTY OUTSIDE THESE WALLS.

"LOREEN WILL OWE HER SAFETY AND SALVATION TO YOUR GENEROUS HEART...

"...AND I FOR ONE TRULY BELIEVE THAT JESUS HIMSELF WOULD DO EXACTLY WHAT YOU'VE DONE TONIGHT."

46

THAT SUNDAY...

"...AND JESUS REPLIED,' THINK NOT THAT I HAVE COME TO BRING PEACE, RATHER I BRING A SWORD.

"'SONS SHALL TURN AGAINST FATHERS, BROTHERS AGAINST BROTHERS, AND MOTHERS AGAINST DAUGHTERS.

"'AS THIS HAPPENS AMONGST YOU, REJOICE AND BE GLAD, MANY WILL BE PERSECUTED FOR MY SAKE--AND THEIR REWARD WILL BE GREAT IN HEAVEN!'"

I CHOSE THIS PARTICULAR PASSAGE BECAUSE I KNOW THAT MANY OF YOU ARE FACING *DIFFICULTIES* WITHIN YOUR FAMILIES OVER OUR *PLEDGE*.

BOTH MISS PAGE AND MR. POWERS ARE UNABLE TO ATTEND OUR WEEKLY MEETING FOR THOSE REASONS. MR. JASPER CHASE, AS MANY OF YOU KNOW, HAS A NEW *BEST-SELLING* NOVEL IN THE BOOK STORES, AND IS BUSILY PENNING A SEQUEL.

ALL THREE OF OUR FRIENDS HAVE ASKED ME TO EXPRESS THEIR REGRETS FOR NOT ATTENDING TODAY'S SERVICE.

NOW ON TO NEWS OF OUR *PROGRESS*. DR. DONALD MARSH OF LINCOLN COLLEGE HAS AN *ANNOUNCEMENT* TO MAKE.

THANK YOU, REVEREND.

MY FRIENDS, OUR CITY OFFICIALS ARE *CORRUPT*, CONTROLLED BY MONEY FROM THE SLUM LORDS AND SALOON OWNERS!

FOR MY LAST DECADE AS COLLEGE PRESIDENT, I HAVE LIVED OUT OF TOUCH AND WITHOUT SYMPATHY FOR PEOPLE IN OUR TOWN. I PROMISE I WILL *NO LONGER* DO SO.

I AM TAKING MY PLACE IN THE COMING PRIMARIES, AND IF *ELECTED* I WILL PLAN A CAMPAIGN TO *RID* OUR COMMUNITY OF ITS POLITICAL CRIMINAL ELEMENT!

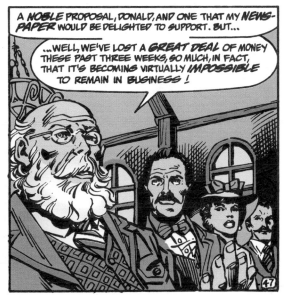

A *NOBLE* PROPOSAL, DONALD, AND ONE THAT MY *NEWSPAPER* WOULD BE DELIGHTED TO SUPPORT. BUT...

...WELL, WE'VE LOST A *GREAT DEAL* OF MONEY THESE PAST THREE WEEKS, SO MUCH, IN FACT, THAT IT'S BECOMING VIRTUALLY *IMPOSSIBLE* TO REMAIN IN BUSINESS!

HOW AWFUL, MR. NORMAN! HAVE SUBSCRIPTIONS FALLEN OFF SO *DRASTICALLY*?

NO, NOT THE SUBSCRIBERS SO MUCH, BUT MAINLY THE *ADVERTISERS*. I *PURPOSELY* DROPPED THE TOBACCO AND ALCOHOL ADS *MYSELF* BUT MOST OF THE REPUTABLE ADVERTISERS HAVE LEFT ON THEIR OWN.

MANY HAVE ACCUSED ME OF *CENSORSHIP* EVER SINCE I'VE ABSTAINED FROM DWELLING ON GOSSIP AND VIOLENCE, CONCENTRATING INSTEAD ON MORALISTIC ESSAYS AND HONEST POLITICS.

I...FEAR I WILL LOSE *EVERYTHING*, BUT... I'M ABSOLUTELY *CONVINCED* I'VE DONE WHAT JESUS WOULD DO IN MY PLACE.

I *TOO* BELIEVE THAT, MY FRIEND. DON'T LOSE HEART, GOD WILL NOT ABANDON YOU.

I'M CONFIDENT THAT THE *DAILY NEWS* WILL SURVIVE, AND EVEN *PROSPER* UNDER YOUR PLAN! ALL YOU NEED IS THE NECESSARY *FINANCING* TO REESTABLISH YOUR LOST ADVERTISERS!

HOW MUCH DO YOU *NEED*, MR. NORMAN?

I AM READY TO PUT A *HALF A MILLION DOLLARS* INTO YOUR PAPER ON ONE CONDITION...

...THAT IT BE CARRIED ON *EXACTLY* IN THE MANNER YOU'VE PLANNED.

48

MISS PAGE, I...I DON'T KNOW WHAT TO SAY--! HOW CAN I POSSIBLY *THANK* YOU...?

PLEASE, MR. NORMAN...DON'T THINK OF THIS AS AN ACT OF *GENEROSITY*.

LATELY, I'VE COME TO KNOW THAT MY WEALTH ISN'T TRULY MINE--IT BELONGS TO *GOD*.

THE FACT IS, WE *NEED* SUCH A NEWSPAPER AS A SYMBOL TO CHAMPION OUR *PLEDGE*.

SO PLEASE, *DON'T* THANK ME.

MERELY *ACCEPT* WHAT GOD HAS FREELY GIVEN!

49

ELECTION DAY, ONE MONTH LATER...

VOTE DONALD MARSH FOR MAYOR

DONALD MARSH VICTORY SPEECH

--THY WAYS AND WORKS, CRE-A-TOR, LORD, MAKE DAYS OF PEACE A-CHIEV-ING.

THE MIGHT-Y VOICE CAN STILL THE SWORD AND WAYS OF WRATH PREVAIL-ING. WITH FAITH AND TRUST IN GOD, WHO RULES BY MIGHT AND ROD, NO MAN NEED EV-ER FEAR, THE GOD OF HOSTS IS NEAR...

...O GOD OF HOSTS DE-FEND US!

WELCOME, MY FRIENDS! WELCOME!

PLEASE COME IN! THERE'S PLENTY OF ROOM!

MY FRIENDS, IT GIVES ME GREAT PLEASURE TO INTRODUCE MR. DONALD MARSH-- --THE **NEXT MAYOR** OF RAYMOND!

CLAP CLAP CLAP CLAP CLAP CLAP CLAP CLAP

THANK YOU FOR YOUR SHOW OF SUPPORT.

I'M AFRAID THE GOOD REVEREND'S STATEMENT IS A BIT *PREMATURE*, AS THE FINAL VOTES HAVE YET TO BE COUNTED. STILL, I'M ASSURED BY MY OFFICE THAT THE OUTCOME OF THIS ELECTION LOOKS *PROMISING*.

MY MAIN FOCUS IN THIS CAMPAIGN HAS CONCENTRATED ON THE ABSOLUTE *ELIMINATION* OF THE SALE OF ALCOHOL IN RAYMOND.

WITHOUT SALOONS OR TAVERNS OUR CITIZENS WILL BE MORE RESPONSIBLE, AND OUR STREETS WILL BE *SAFER*. FOR WITHOUT THE DEGRADING TEMPTATION OF LIQUOR...

...WE WILL REMAIN *FREE* TO PURSUE MORE PROFITABLE IDEALS.

NOW THIS NEEDN'T MEAN LOSING ANY PERSONAL FREEDOM, *EXCEPT* THE FREEDOM TO ACT IRRESPONSIBLY!

WITH GOD'S HELP WE NEED ONLY TO--

THERE! THAT'S HIM!!

51

DR. WEST...WHAT ABOUT MR. MARSH AND REVEREND MAXWELL~? WHAT IF THEY'RE *HURT*?!

SOON AS YOU'RE ALL SAFE, I'LL TRY AND GO BACK IN FOR THEM!

QUICKLY, NOW! THE STREET IS *CLEAR*!

I KNOW THESE PEOPLE! THEY WON'T GIVE UP! WE'RE NOT SAFE!

HURRY!

HERE THEY COME!

VIRGINIA, *LOOKOUT*!

KR-RAK!

UGGH~!

53

...GOD... BLESS YOU.

GO BACK WHERE YA CAME FROM!

WE DON'T WANT YA HERE!

HEAVENLY FATHER, MAY THE SOUL OF THY DAUGHTER, LOREEN RUTH DAVIS, FIND PEACE IN THY ETERNAL KEEPING.

AND GRANT US CONSOLATION, OH LORD, AS WE COMMEND HER BODY TO THE EARTH FROM WHICH IT CAME.

ASHES TO ASHES...

...DUST TO DUST.

AMEN.

RACHEL--? AREN'T YOU RIDING HOME WITH US?

NOT THIS TIME, ROLLIN. TAKE CARE OF YOUR SISTER. I'LL SEE YOU BOTH SOON.

WE... ...WE'LL BE WAITING FOR YOU.

RACHEL--?! JASPER CHASE! I THOUGHT IT WAS YOU. WHAT'RE YOU DOING OUT HERE?

I, UH, NEEDED REFERENCE MATERIAL FOR MY NEW NOVEL... THERE'S A FUNERAL IN IT, YOU SEE, AND...

...I-I'M SORRY, RACHEL. I DIDN'T MEAN TO BE DISRESPECTFUL, OR TO INTRUDE ON THE GROUP...

IT'S YOUR GROUP, TOO. YOU'RE ALWAYS WELCOME, JASPER.

YEAH, WELL, I GUESS I JUST DON'T HAVE THE TIME I USED TO.

LOOK, RACHEL, THERE'S NO POINT IN PRETENDING. I CAME HERE HOPING TO SEE YOU--

--AND TO GIVE YOU THIS!

IT'S MY *FIRST* BOOK. I WROTE IT FOR *YOU.*

GOT TO GO NOW.

I HAVE A *DEADLINE.*

LATER...

THE TITLE *DOESN'T* SURPRISE ME, RACHEL.

I'VE ALWAYS SUSPECTED THAT JASPER CHASE WAS *IN LOVE* WITH YOU.

AND ONCE I THOUGHT I LOVED *HIM,* BUT THE WAY HE SPOKE TODAY...SO *COLD* AND *BITTER.*

I COULD *NEVER* MARRY A MAN LIKE HIM.

I'M RELIEVED TO HEAR THAT, RACHEL.

I'M NOT JUDGING HIM, BUT JASPER HAS SUDDENLY BECOME A *BEST-SELLING* AUTHOR AND THIS FIRST TASTE OF SUCCESS HAS *BLINDED* HIM TO HIS PLEDGE.

ROLLIN AND I PROBABLY KNOW BETTER THAN ANYONE THAT MONEY CAN BE A VERY *POWERFUL* DISTRACTION.

HAVE YOU SEEN THE MORNING PAPER?

MAMA READ THE HEADLINES TO ME.

POOR MR. MARSH. LOSING THE ELECTION MUST'VE BEEN A *TERRIBLE* BLOW TO HIM.

THE TOWN WILL *SUFFER* MORE BECAUSE OF IT.

58

TRUE. HOWEVER, THE ELECTION WAS WON BY A VERY *MEAGER* MAJORITY VOTE. NEXT TIME THINGS COULD BE *DIFFERENT*.

BUT WHAT ABOUT *NOW*, GINNY?! IT WAS THE *SALOONS* THAT ACTUALLY KILLED LOREEN! THERE MUST BE *SOMETHING* WE CAN DO!

ACTUALLY, I *HAVE* DECIDED ON A PLAN TO HELP PEOPLE LIKE LOREEN TO A *BETTER* WAY OF LIFE.

I'M GOING TO BUY UP *PROPERTY* IN THE RECTANGLE.

THERE ARE FUNDS ENOUGH FOR BUILDING CLEAN NEW RESIDENCES, A HOSPITAL, PERHAPS EVEN A *MUSIC COLLEGE* WHERE YOU CAN SING AND TEACH!

GINNY, THIS... THIS IS *WONDERFUL!* BUT CAN YOU AFFORD IT? YOU'VE GIVEN MR. NORMAN'S NEWSPAPER SO *MUCH* ALREADY!

NO, I COULDN'T DO IT ALONE, BUT I WON'T HAVE TO.

THIS WAS *ROLLIN'S* IDEA! YOU SEE? HE'S GIVEN ME *HALF* OF HIS INHERITANCE FOR US TO BEGIN!

ROLLIN? ROLLIN DID THIS...?

SIS, ARE YOU FEELING BET--

--OH! I'M SORRY. I THOUGHT YOU WERE ALONE.

PLEASE STAY, ROLLIN. I WAS JUST LEAVING.

THANK YOU, ROLLIN.

PARDON--?

FOR YOUR HELP DURING THE RIOT.

YOU SAVED MY LIFE.

THANK YOU.

DON'T LOOK SO SURPRISED, ROLLIN. RACHEL IS IMPRESSED, SHE LIKES THE CHANGE IN YOU.

WHY DIDN'T YOU SPEAK TO HER? YOU ACTED AS IF SHE WAS A STRANGER!

LETTER FROM FATHER CALVIN BRUCE, PASTOR OF OUR LADY OF CONSOLATION, TO BISHOP PHILIP CAXTON, ARCHDIOCESE OF CHICAGO.

"MY DEAR PHILIP..."

"...IT IS LATE SUNDAY NIGHT, AND I'M TIRED BUT ALSO INTENSELY AWAKE AND OVERFLOWING WITH ANXIETY."

FOR SALE BY OWNER

"REGARDLESS OF THE HOUR, I FEEL DRIVEN TO WRITE YOU A PERSONAL ACCOUNT OF THE REMARKABLE SITUATION WHICH I HAVE RECENTLY STUDIED IN RAYMOND, VIRGINIA."

"THIS LARGELY CONCERNS AN OLD PROTESTANT FRIEND, REV. HENRY MAXWELL, WHO ENTERED THE SEMINARY WHEN I WAS MAKING MY VOWS."

61

"I WAS QUITE STUNNED DURING A RECENT VISIT AS HENRY DESCRIBED TO ME AN ASTOUNDING PROPOSAL HE HAD MADE TO HIS CONGREGATION A YEAR BEFORE...

"...ASKING FOR VOLUNTEERS TO ACT FOR A FULL YEAR EXACTLY AS THEY FEEL CHRIST WOULD.

"THE EFFECTS OF THIS HAVE BEEN ASTOUNDING.

"EVEN MORE STRIKING IS THE STORY OF VIRGINIA AND ROLLIN PAGE, SIBLING HEIRS TO AN IMMENSE FAMILY FORTUNE. MISS PAGE HAS GIVEN WHOLLY AND SELFLESSLY, USING HER WEALTH AND GREAT HEART TO THE BETTERMENT OF THE POOR IN RAYMOND.

"NO DOUBT YOU'VE FOLLOWED THE NATIONWIDE NEWSPAPER ACCOUNTS OF FORMER RAILROAD EXECUTIVE ALEXANDER POWERS. WHEN HIS VOW COMPELLED HIM TO ACT UPON EVIDENCE OF CRIMINAL ACTIVITY WITHIN THE COMPANY, POWERS LOST HIS JOB, SOCIAL POSITION, AND EVEN HIS OWN FAMILY HAVE SINCE ABANDONED HIM.

"EDWARD NORMAN, DAILY NEWS OWNER AND EDITOR, HAS RISKED HIS ENTIRE BUSINESS IN HIS SOLEMN OBEDIENCE TO THE PLEDGE. IN EFFECT, HE HAS CREATED ONE OF THE MOST SUCCESSFUL AND INTERESTING NEWSPAPERS IN THIS NATION, COMPOSED ALMOST ENTIRELY OF CHRISTIAN PHILOSOPHY.

"HER BROTHER, ROLLIN, IS A MORE RECENT CONVERT. HE CONTINUES TO DEVOTE THE LAST OF HIS MILLIONS TOWARD THE CONSTRUCTION OF NEW SCHOOLS AND HOSPITALS IN THE MOST POVERTY-STRICKEN AREAS OF THE CITY.

*"PERHAPS MOST REMARKABLE OF ALL IS RACHEL WINSLOW.

"NEVER HAVE I HEARD A MORE MIRACULOUS SINGING VOICE. TRUE TO HER PLEDGE, SHE HAS LONG SINCE ABANDONED THE CERTAINTY OF A LUCRATIVE CAREER, USING HER GIFT SOLELY FOR THE INSPIRATIONAL RICHNESS OF OTHERS.

"LAST SUNDAY I SAT SPELL-BOUND IN HENRY'S CHURCH. ALWAYS A FINE SPEAKER, HE HAS DRAMATICALLY BECOME EVEN MORE POWERFUL IN DELIVERING HIS CONVICTIONS.

"THE EFFECT OF HIS SERMON ON THE CONGREGATION WAS FILLED WITH MORE CHRISTIAN LOVE THAN ANYTHING I HAVE EVER BEFORE BEHELD.

"RAYMOND IS NOW A DIFFERENT TOWN, KINDER AND GENTLER, THAN I'VE EVER KNOWN.

"MORE THAN ONCE, I WAS ACTUALLY MOVED TO TEARS.

*"MY VISIT TO RAYMOND HAS CHALLENGED MY OWN PRINCIPLES AND DEDICATION TO CHRIST, AND THAT OF MY PARISH.

"I ASK FOR YOUR PRAYERS, PHILIP, AS MY BISHOP AND AS MY FRIEND. HELP ME AND MY FLOCK TO FIND THE COURAGE AND CONVICTION TO ACT UPON THAT SAME QUESTION...

"...WHAT WOULD JESUS DO?"

THE THEATER DISTRICT OF CHICAGO.

COME ON, FELICIA! WHAT'RE YOU WAITING FOR? SHALL I *FREEZE* TO DEATH WHILE YOU *DAYDREAM?!*

BUY A FL-FLOWER, MA'AM?

THEY'RE VERY LOVELY!

HERE YOU ARE!

GOSH--! T-THANKS, LADY!

YOU'RE ONLY MAKING A *FOOL* OF YOURSELF, YOU KNOW. THEY *DON'T* APPRECIATE SUCH GENEROSITY.

THAT'S AN EXCELLENT IDEA, ROSE.

WHY DIDN'T YOU INVITE THE FILTHY LITTLE BEAST HOME FOR A *HOT SUPPER?*

DON'T YOU DARE!

SOMETIMES I'M *ASHAMED* THAT YOU'RE MY SISTER!

NOW HURRY UP! THAT HORRID MUSIC HAS LEFT ME *EXHAUSTED!*

LATER THAT EVENING...

OH, POPPA! THE PLAY WAS *WONDERFUL!* I WISH YOU'D GONE WITH US!

DON'T BE *RIDICULOUS,* FELICIA! SOMEONE *HAD* TO STAY WITH MAMMA!

A LETTER CAME FOR YOU, FELICIA. IT'S FROM YOUR COUSIN.

FROM *RACHEL*-?! PERHAPS SHE'S COMING TO *VISIT!*

WELL, COME ON, FELICIA! SHE'S MY COUSIN, TOO! WHAT'S THE LATEST *NEWS*?!

RACHEL SAYS THAT OUR PASTOR, FATHER BRUCE, VISITED THEIR CHURCH LAST SUNDAY!

SEEMS HE WAS VERY MUCH INTERESTED IN THEIR *PLEDGE!*

THAT AGAIN! THAT SILLY PLEDGE IS ALL RACHEL *EVER* WRITES ABOUT THESE DAYS!

SHE SHOULD COME HERE TO CHICAGO AND ARRANGE A *CONCERT!* WHY SHE CONTINUES TO WASTE HER VOICE IN THAT BACKWARD LITTLE TOWN IS BEYOND ME!

THOSE PEOPLE COULDN'T POSSIBLY *APPRECIATE* HER! DON'T YOU AGREE, POPPA?

YES, YES OF COURSE, THAT PLEDGE IS QUITE IMPRACTICAL...

...NOW IF YOU'LL BOTH EXCUSE ME, I HAVE SOME WORK TO FINISH IN TOWN!

65

"ROSE, DON'T YOU THINK POPPA HAS BEEN ACTING A LITTLE *STRANGE,* LATELY?"

POPPA *NEVER WORKS* SATURDAY NIGHTS! HE'S BECOME SO *DISTANT!*

I HAVEN'T NOTICED ANYTHING.

I'M GOING TO *BED.* BE A DEAR AND LOOK IN ON MAMA, WON'T YOU? I'M *TOO TIRED* TO BE AGREEABLE.

MAMA--? ARE YOU AWAKE...?

COME IN, CHILD.

I'M *HAPPY* YOU'RE UP! I BROUGHT SOMETHING FOR YOU!

FELICIA, CHILD, I... I'M *FRIGHTENED...*

FRIGHTENED, MAMA? BUT WHY--

IT'S YOUR *FATHER--!*

SINCE I'VE BECOME ILL HE...HE'S *CHANGED!* HE WON'T TALK TO ME, OR EVEN LOOK AT ME!

PLEASE TELL ME, BABY, WHAT SHOULD I *DO?!*

66

THE STERLING ESTATE.

THE GIRLS ARE LATE.

IT'S BETTER THIS WAY.

--NUH-HNNN...?

ROB... ROBERT...?

ROBERT? IS THAT YOU--?

ROBERT? ARE YOU OUT THERE?

ROBERT--?

ANSWER ME, ROBERT...

PLEASE...!

FORGIVE ME.

PLEASE, ROBERT! I NEED YOU! YOU MUST TELL ME WHAT'S WRONG! I ONLY WANT TO--

BLAMMM!

THE RECTORY...

PHILIP--! WHAT A PLEASANT SURPRISE! COME IN!

I DECIDED TO REPLY TO YOUR REMARKABLE LETTER IN PERSON, CALVIN.

I BELIEVE WE'VE MUCH TO DISCUSS THIS AFTERNOON.

69

FIRST, LET ME GET YOUR MIND AT EASE.

AS YOUR BISHOP, I WHOLEHEARTEDLY *APPROVE* OF THE STEPS YOU'VE TAKEN TODAY. IN ONLY A FEW HOURS, IT'S ALREADY THE TALK OF THE CITY! I, FOR ONE, WILL SUPPORT YOU TO THE *BEST* OF MY ABILITY AND INFLUENCE!

THAT MEANS MORE TO ME THAN I CAN SAY.

THIS *WILL* PROVE DIFFICULT, YOU KNOW. WE MAY WELL HAVE A *CRISIS* ON OUR HANDS!

AFTER ALL, *MARTYRDOM* HAS BECOME A LOST ART, AND ISN'T *THAT* EXACTLY WHAT IT MEANS TO FOLLOW CHRIST?

OF COURSE, I'LL EXPECT PROBLEMS-- *SERIOUS* ONES! EXCUSE ME A MOMENT...

KNOCK KNOCK

URGENT MESSAGE FOR YOU, FATHER.

THANK YOU.

WHAT IS IT? I'LL WAGER THAT *TROUBLE* IS STARTING ALREADY!

I'M NOT SURE. IT'S FROM ONE OF MY PARISHIONERS...

GOD HELP US!

MR. STERLING HAS *KILLED* HIMSELF...!

70

STERLING
ERIC
BORN 1840 DIED 1899
CHRISTINE
BORN 1846 DIED 1899
BELOVED PARENTS OF
ROSE AND FELICIA

OH, MAMA...

...POPPA...

ROSE AND I ARE ALL *ALONE* NOW... LOST.

WHAT... WHAT'RE WE TO DO...?

YOU'RE *NEVER* ALONE, FELICIA.

RACHEL--!!

OH, RACHEL...

...IT IS REALLY *YOU*...? ARE YOU *REALLY* HERE--?!

NOTHING COULD KEEP ME AWAY, LITTLE COUSIN.

CHRISTINE

71

I'M HERE TO *HELP*, FELICIA. IF YOU'LL LET ME.

WHAT DO YOU INTEND TO DO?

I DON'T KNOW.

THERE HAD BEEN SOMETHING GREATLY *TROUBLING* POPPA FOR MONTHS...EVEN SO, HOW COULD I EVER HAVE EXPECTED *THIS*?

MAMA'S *LONG ILLNESS* HAD ALREADY TAKEN ITS TOLL ON HER... AND POPPA'S *DEATH* WAS JUST *TOO MUCH* FOR HER WEARY HEART TO STAND.

"THE DOUBLE TRAGEDY HAS UTTERLY *TRAUMATIZED* MY POOR SISTER, LEAVING HER COMPLETELY WITHDRAWN. SHE HAS YET TO SPEAK, AND *REFUSED* EVEN TO ATTEND THE FUNERALS."

I KNOW SHE SHOULD BE IN A *HOSPITAL*, BUT I DON'T SEE HOW WE CAN MANAGE THE *EXPENSE*.

BUT YOUR FATHER'S ESTATE SHOULD BE SETTLED IN A FEW DAYS. SURELY THEN--

NO. I...I'M AFRAID NOT.

SEE IT FOR YOURSELF! POPPA GAMBLED AWAY *EVERYTHING*!

WE ARE *RUINED*!!

72

I'M GLAD YOU CAME BY THIS EVENING, PHILIP. I RECEIVED A LETTER FROM *FELICIA STERLING* YESTERDAY, AND I THINK YOU'LL FIND IT MOST *INTERESTING.*

AH, YES. WHAT A *TRAGEDY.* THE ENTIRE FAMILY HAS BEEN IN MY PRAYERS.

HOW IS THE POOR GIRL?

"FELICIA SAYS THAT SHE AND ROSE WERE WARMLY WELCOMED INTO THE HOME OF THEIR AUNT AND COUSIN IN VIRGINIA. ALTHOUGH FELICIA FOUND MUCH SPIRITUAL COMFORT THERE, HER SISTER CONTINUED TO BROOD BITTERLY, REFUSING TO ACCEPT THE GREAT CHANGE IN THEIR LIVES.

"DETERMINED NOT TO OVERLY BURDEN HER RELATIVES, FELICIA FOUND A JOB AS A COOK WITHIN A SHELTER IN THE RECTANGLE. SHE SAYS THAT SHE ENTERED UPON THIS WORK WITH THE KEENEST OF PLEASURE, TAKING GREAT DELIGHT IN KEEPING WITH HER *PLEDGE* BY SACRIFICING HERSELF FOR OTHERS.

"FELICIA SAVED HER MONEY, AND WITHIN A MONTH SHE MANAGED TO MOVE INTO A SIMPLE BOARDING HOUSE TO CARE FOR HER STILL AILING SISTER."

74

IN CLOSING, FELICIA DREAMS OF RETURNING SOON TO CHICAGO AND FINDING SIMILAR WORK IN THE *SLUM DISTRICTS*. SHE PLANS TO TEACH YOUNG MOTHERS HOW TO PROPERLY AND INEXPENSIVELY PREPARE NUTRITIOUS MEALS.

A *REMARKABLE* YOUNG WOMAN! I DOUBT I'VE EVER ENCOUNTERED SOMEONE WITH SUCH *FAITH*!

I HAVE TO CONFESS THAT FELICIA STERLING HAS KEPT HER *PROMISE* TO CHRIST IN A SIMPLER YET GREATER SENSE THAN I EVER HAVE ATTEMPTED!

WHY, SHE'S ACTUALLY *INSPIRING*!

SADLY, THE SAME IS NOT TRUE FOR MY-SELF.

I'VE YET TO SATISFY MY *OWN* PROMISE TO OUR LORD. MY LIFE HERE AS PASTOR HAS BEEN FAR TOO LUXURIOUS, AND I KNOW I SHOULD ASK FOR *REASSIGNMENT*!

BUT WHERE? AND TO DO *WHAT*--?!

AS BISHOP, I BELIEVE I CAN HELP US *BOTH*, OLD FRIEND.

YOU SEE, I HAVE A *PLAN*.

GIVE ME A MOMENT TO CHANGE.

WHAT'S YOUR PLAN?

IT'S ALREADY BEEN SET INTO MOTION THROUGH CARDINAL LUCKETT.

BRIEFLY, MY PLAN INVOLVES RE-LOCATING *MYSELF* INTO THE VERY CENTER OF THE MOST *WICKED* AND THE MOST *NEED-FUL* SECTION OF THIS CITY.

ONCE THERE, I INTEND TO SURROUND MYSELF WITH *HUMAN MISERY,* TRUSTING GOD TO GUIDE ME IN MAKING SOME GOOD USE OUT OF THE *REST* OF MY LIFE FOR THE SAKE OF OTHERS, AND FOR *HIS* GREATER GLORY!

A *NOBLE* PROPOSITION, PHILIP! AND *EXACTLY* THE KIND OF THING I'VE BEEN *PRAYING* FOR-- IF YOU'LL HAVE ME!

OF COURSE I WILL, OLD FRIEND!

I'D BEST BE GOING AND GET STARTED ON THE NECESSARY ARRANGE-MENTS.

GOD BE WITH YOU!

GIT READY. SOMEBODY'S COMIN'...

WHA--?!

SHUT UP, GRAMPS.

NO NOISE AN' YA WON'T GIT HURT.

76

77

79

M-MY LEG...! OH GOD... UGGH...

VINCE... ₹! THE GUN... IT--IT JUST WENT OFF...! I SWEAR!

I DIDN'T MEAN IT, VINCE. OH, GOD, *HELP* ME! I CAN'T LIVE LIKE THIS ANY MORE

GOD HEARS YOUR PRAYERS, MY SON, AND IF YOU *TRULY* MEAN IT, HE *WILL* CHANGE YOUR LIFE... AND VINCE'S LIFE.

I--I DO MEAN IT, SIR. PLEASE... HELP US... HELP JIMMY. HE'S MY PAL.

...NNGH... UHHH...

...TH-THAT YOU, BISHOP... ₹ STREETS ARE ... *DANGEROUS* AFTER D-DARK, ...UNNPHH...

...YOU SHOULDN'T HAVE COME HERE...

YOU'RE WRONG, MY SON.

THIS IS EXACTLY WHERE I SHOULD BE.

THE NEW SETTLEMENT HALL, FORMERLY THE SITE OF THE WHITE CROSS CHRISTIAN MISSION, CHRISTMAS EVE...

WHAT WOULD JESUS DO?

THAT WAS THE PLEDGE PROMISED BY A SMALL GROUP OF MY CONGREGATION JUST FOURTEEN MONTHS AGO.

WITHIN THAT SPACE OF TIME OUR VOW HAS BECOME KNOWN BY THE ENTIRE NATION AND INDEED, BY MOST OF THE CHRISTIAN WORLD AS WELL!

AS A RESULT OF THIS EFFORT, THE POVERTY-STRICKEN DISTRICTS OF OUR TOWN HAVE BEEN *MIRACULOUSLY TRANSFORMED,* WITH THEIR CRIMINAL ELEMENT ALL BUT *ABOLISHED!*

TONIGHT, WE WISH TO DEDICATE THIS NEW BUILDING TO OUR *INSPIRATION...* A STRANGER WHO INSTILLED IN US A DESIRE FOR TRUE GENEROSITY AND CHRISTIAN SACRIFICE!

WE ALL OWE HIM A *TREMENDOUS DEBT!*

MAY GOD *REST* HIS SOUL!

REVEREND, PLEASE! I WANT TO SPEAK!

81

I...I JUST WANT TO SAY THAT I *KNEW* THIS MAN YOU SPOKE OF. WE ONCE WORKED TOGETHER AS PRINTERS.

HE--HE'D LOANED ME TWENTY DOLLARS WHEN I LOST MY JOB. SIX MONTHS LATER I'D HEARD HE WAS OUT OF WORK, *TOO.*

"BY THEN I WAS IN A *BAD WAY*... SICK AND HOMELESS ON THE STREETS. EVERYDAY CHURCHGOERS, LIKE MOST OF YOU, SAW ME AND DID *NOTHING.* OF COURSE, I NEVER REALLY EXPECTED *ANYONE* TO HELP.

"SO...MAYBE YOU CAN IMAGINE MY *SURPRISE* WHEN I WAS RESCUED BY THE *SAME MAN* WHO'D HELPED ME BEFORE.

"NEARLY AS *DESTITUTE* AS MYSELF, HE GAVE ME SHELTER AND HIS WIFE NURSED ME BACK TO HEALTH. I LEARNED SOMETIME LATER THEY WERE *EVICTED,* AND THAT HIS WIFE HAD *DIED.* "

I TRIED TO FIND HIM...TO THANK HIM...

...I *NEVER GOT* THE CHANCE.

BAH! SO MUCH FOR *CHRISTIAN CHARITY!*

I HAVE A *QUESTION* FOR THE REVEREND--IF HE *DARES* TO ANSWER IT!

82

BY ALL MEANS, GOOD SIR. OF COURSE, I CAN'T PROMISE THAT MY ANSWER WILL *SATISFY* YOU.

I WANT TO KNOW WHAT JESUS WOULD DO IN *MY* CASE!

I HAVEN'T WORKED IN *TWO MONTHS!* MY FAMILY IS TORN APART, CLOSE TO *STARVING!*

IS IT MY FAULT THAT THERE'S NO WORK FOR ME?! EVERYWHERE I GO THERE IS *NOTHING!*

WHAT WOULD JESUS DO IF HE WAS *OUTTA WORK* LIKE ME?! HUH?!

WHAT WOULD HE DO?!

WHAT WOULD JESUS DO IN YOUR PLACE...?

I...I'M AFRAID THAT I CAN'T SAY, MY POOR FRIEND. PERHAPS THERE IS A *CHRISTIAN* IN THE ROOM WHO HAS BEEN IN THIS CONDITION, AND HAS *TRIED* TO DO AS JESUS WOULD...?

IF SO, HE COULD ANSWER YOU BETTER THAN I.

THIS IS ALL *NON-SENSE!*

THIS IS *NOT* A PROBLEM FOR *RELIGION!* OUR ENTIRE *SOCIAL SYSTEM* IS AT FAULT!

83

{sigh} THIS IS **NOT** A POLITICAL MEETING, MR. CARLSEN. BUT PLEASE GO AHEAD, AND HAVE YOUR SAY.

GOOD CITIZENS! MY **SOCIALIST PARTY** WOULD **NEVER** ALLOW SUCH TRAVESTIES TO HAPPEN!

IT IS **NOT** YOUR FAULT THAT YOU LIVE IN AN AGE THAT PERMITS **CAPITALISTIC GREED** TO COME BEFORE THE WELFARE OF INNOCENT MEN, WOMEN AND CHILDREN!

I THANK GOD, IF THERE **IS** A GOD--WHICH I VERY MUCH DOUBT--THAT I, MYSELF, HAVE NEVER **DARED** TO HAVE A FAMILY!

BEG YOUR PARDON, SON...

EHH--?!

...I BELIEVE MY AGE MAKES ME MORE **QUALIFIED** TO ANSWER THE REVEREND'S QUESTION THAN YOU.

WHAT WOULD JESUS DO IN *MY* CASE?

I DON'T KNOW.

I CAN ONLY SAY THAT HIS *EXAMPLE* HAS MADE ME A *BETTER MAN* THAN I EVER COULD'VE BEEN WITHOUT HIM.

RIDICULOUS! ARE WE HERE TO TAKE THE WORD OF FANATICS--?

SO HE CLAIMS TO BE A CHRISTIAN!

THIS COUNTRY HAS THOUSANDS LIKE HIM WHO GO TO CHURCH AND SING THEIR HYMNS--AND HAVE ALL THE LUXURIES AND COMFORTS OTHERS ARE *DENIED*!

I'M TELLING YOU, DON'T EXPECT REFORM TO COME OUT OF THE CHURCHES!

WE NEED A NEW WAY OF GOVERNMENT--

ROLLIN--?

ROLLIN! WAIT!

RACHEL--? YOU--YOU'D BETTER GO BACK INSIDE; IT'S **COLD** OUT HERE.

WHAT **IS** IT, ROLLIN ? THE PAST FEW DAYS YOU'VE SEEMED SO **TROUBLED**... I **SAW** YOUR FACE AS YOU LEFT THE MEETING !

PLEASE--DON'T KEEP THIS FROM ME ! WON'T YOU TELL ME WHAT'S WORRYING YOU...?!

I'M SURPRISED YOU HAVEN'T **GUESSED**...

HERE ! LOOK AT IT !

MY **LAST** TWENTY DOLLAR GOLD PIECE !

THE **SOLE REMAINING REMNANT** OF MY MILLION DOLLAR INHERITANCE !

MY MONEY HAS HELPED **TRANS-FORM** THE RECTANGLE ! I'VE BUILT A SCHOOL, HOSPITAL, NEW RESIDENCES...BRINGING **HOPE** BACK INTO THIS POOR PLACE THE ONLY WAY I KNEW HOW !

NOW I'M **BROKE,** ALMOST PENNILESS, AND THERE'S STILL SO MUCH TO **DO** !

I GUESS I EXPECTED TO CONTINUE USING MY **MONEY** TO HELP OTHERS. BUT **NOW**... WHAT CAN I DO ?

BUT ROLLIN, THAT'S NOT TRUE! YES, YOU'VE DONE *WONDERFUL* THINGS, BUT IT WASN'T JUST YOUR MONEY!

YOUR *HEART AND SOUL* WENT INTO EVERY PROJECT!

EVERYONE SERVES GOD IN THEIR *OWN* WAY.

EVELYN DAVIS HOUSE
QUALITY LOWES
RENT ROOMS FOR

*YOUR SISTER'S WEALTH HAS ALSO DIMINISHED, BUT VIRGINIA'S NURTURING NATURE WILL *ALWAYS* BE OF SERVICE HERE IN THE RECTANGLE.

"HER LOVING TALENT FOR REACHING OUT TO THE HELPLESS GOES BEYOND MONEY.

"DONALD MARSH WILL DOUBTLESSLY CONTINUE TO ENGAGE HIS INTELLECT AND POLITICAL INFLUENCE TO *PURIFY* THIS CITY.

*AND THINK OF THE SPIRITUAL *STRENGTH* OF ALEXANDER POWERS. HE HAS LOST A LUCRATIVE CAREER, AND THE RESPECT OF HIS FAMILY THROUGH HIS PROMISE TO OUR LORD. BUT, EVEN SO, HE MANAGES TO CARRY HIMSELF WITH DIGNITY AND CLEAN CHRISTIAN HONOR.

BY VIRTUE OF HIS FAITH AND MORALITY, EDWARD NORMAN HAS CREATED A *FORCE* IN JOURNALISM THAT WILL MOLD *CHRISTIAN* PRINCIPLES ALL ACROSS THE NATION.

"MY COUSIN, FELICIA STERLING, LIVES A HAPPY PRODUCTIVE LIFE IN CHICAGO, DEDICATED TO BRINGING A PERSONAL TOUCH OF *HOME* TO THE POOR TENEMENTS OF THAT CITY."

"SHE IS FULLY DEVOTED TO HER SISTER, ROSE, WHO REMAINS IN *DESPAIR* OVER THE LOSS OF THEIR PARENTS AND THEIR FORTUNE. I SUSPECT SHE WILL REMAIN DEPENDENT ON FELICIA FOR A LONG TIME TO COME."

"THINK OF JASPER CHASE. HE GAVE UP ON HIS PLEDGE."

"HIS BOOKS CONTINUE TO BE POPULAR SUCCESSES, BUT THERE IS A COLD, CYNICAL STING TO THEM QUITE *UNLIKE* THE MAN WE ONCE KNEW."

THE LIE

A NOVEL BY

ER CHASE

AND YOU, RACHEL. YOUR *VOICE* WILL ALWAYS *ENDURE*, LIGHTING UP THE SLUMS AND DRAWING LOST SOULS BACK TO GOD. YOU'RE RIGHT. OURS IS AN *UNENDING* CALL TO SERVE GOD IN ANY WAY WE CAN. AND RACHEL, I --

EXCUSE ME, PLEASE--?

SORRY TO BOTHER YOU. WE ARE *STRANGERS*, NEWLY ARRIVED FROM RICHMOND. I'VE MOVED MY FAMILY HERE IN SEARCH OF WORK.

WE...WE CAN'T SEEM TO FIND A *VACANCY* IN AN AFFORDABLE HOTEL, AND I WAS WONDERING IF PERHAPS YOU COULD *SUGGEST* A PLACE?

I'M AFRAID THEY'RE ALL *FULL* FOR THE HOLIDAYS... AHH--WAIT JUST A MOMENT! I THINK I *DO* KNOW A PLACE--!

TRY THE RAYMOND HOTEL TWO BLOCKS OVER ON ST. LOUIS AVENUE. IT'S *BRAND NEW* AND VERY COMFORTABLE.

OF COURSE, YOU'RE LIKELY TO FIND IT RATHER *EXPENSIVE*, SO PERHAPS YOU'D BETTER TAKE THIS WITH YOU.

B-BUT, SIR... I COULDN'T POSSIBLY...

OF COURSE YOU CAN.

WON'T YOU TELL ME YOUR NAME, SO I CAN *REPAY* YOU?!

UNNECESSARY! DO THE *SAME* FOR *SOMEONE ELSE* SOMEDAY!

MERRY CHRISTMAS!

90

OH, ROLLIN--THAT WAS *WONDERFUL!*

IT...IT WAS ONLY TWENTY DOLLARS, RACHEL.

BUT IT WAS *ALL* YOU HAD--!

ROLLIN! YOU *STILL* HAVE MUCH TO *GIVE!* THAT COIN WAS ALL THE MONEY YOU HAD, AND YOU DIDN'T EVEN THINK TWICE BEFORE GIVING IT AWAY!

YOU'VE *CHANGED,* ROLLIN! YOU'VE BEEN *BLESSED* GREATER THAN ALL OF US...

...AND I *LOVE* YOU FOR IT!

YOU DO LOVE ME--? BUT RACHEL, I'M POOR NOW! *PENNILESS!*

NO, YOU'RE NOT...

YOU'RE THE *RICHEST* MAN I KNOW!

(91)